D0525747

COPING WITH
CORONAVIRUS

This book is dedicated to all who are affected by coronavirus and all who care for them.

Royalties from the sale of this book will be donated to medical charities assisting with the global response to coronavirus.

Dr Brendan Kelly

COPING WITH CORONAVIRUS

HOW TO STAY CALM AND PROTECT YOUR MENTAL HEALTH

A PSYCHOLOGICAL TOOLKIT

MERRION
PRESS

First published in 2020 by
Merrion Press
10 George's Street
Newbridge
Co. Kildare
Ireland
www.merrionpress.ie

9781785373640 (Paper)
9781785373619 (Kindle)
9781785373626 (Epub)
9781785373633 (PDF)

Brendan Kelly was born in Galway and is Professor of Psychiatry at Trinity College Dublin and Consultant Psychiatrist at Tallaght University Hospital, Dublin. In addition to his medical degree (MB BCh BAO), he holds masters degrees in healthcare management (MA) and Buddhist studies (MA); and doctorates in medicine (MD), history (PhD), governance (DGov) and law (PhD). He also has a masters degree (MSc) in epidemiology, the study of the distribution and determinants of disease, from London School of Hygiene and Tropical Medicine. Brendan has written and co-written over 250 scientific papers, 500 articles in newspapers and journals, and 11 books, including *Hearing Voices: The History of Psychiatry in Ireland*. He is a regular contributor to radio and print media and writes a blog for *Psychology Today*.

Contents

What to do if you think you have coronavirus

- If you think you have coronavirus, immediately contact a medical practitioner, health authority or emergency service in your area by telephone.
- If you have been to a place where there is spread of coronavirus and you are not feeling well, check if you have symptoms of coronavirus: cough, shortness of breath, breathing difficulties and/or fever (high temperature).
- If you have symptoms of coronavirus, phone your doctor or local emergency department (ED) without delay. Do not go to your doctor or ED. Phone them first. Tell them about your symptoms. Give them the details about your situation. Follow their advice.
- Avoid contact with other people by self-isolating.

Introduction

Coronavirus presents the world with two problems. The first problem is the illness caused by the new coronavirus itself, COVID-19. The second problem is the anxiety and panic that the virus triggers in the minds of virtually everyone who hears about it.

Both problems are very real and both can be solved.

The solution to the first problem – the illness itself – lies in the hands of health authorities and the governments that fund them at global, national and local levels. All around the world, medical staff are using established methods of infection control and treatments that were developed during previous outbreaks and are being adapted to this new challenge. These efforts involve a mixture of past experience and new learning as the novel coronavirus slowly but inevitably reveals its secrets. Ultimately, coronavirus will be controlled.

This book concerns the second problem, which is far more widespread than the virus itself and which will likely persist long after this particular virus has passed. This problem is anxiety and panic. Right across the globe, people are worried, often deeply so. Some are panicked. Others are paralysed by fear.

There are many questions. Will I catch coronavirus? Will a family member die from the infection? How obsessional should I be about washing my hands? How can I be extra-cautious? Should I wear a face mask? What about my children? How will this affect me financially? Even if this threat passes, will this happen again? Will there be a new coronavirus this year? What about next year?

The anxiety triggered by the new coronavirus can take many forms. Some people are just generally worried about catching the virus and its impact on their family life, their country's economy and the world in general. Others experience full-blown panic attacks, overwhelmed by a sudden sense of impending doom that now has a name: coronavirus. And, perhaps most commonly, a great number of people have developed a persistent sense of unease, a brooding hopelessness or – at worst – a feeling of helplessness and nihilism: If we cannot control this virus, then what else can we not control? Is our entire way of life changing forever? Will anything ever be the same?

All of these responses are understandable, but many are either unhelpful or misguided, or both. As a psychiatrist, I am accustomed to treating people with all kinds of anxiety: panic disorder, phobias, social anxiety, generalised anxiety, post-traumatic stress disorder and many other conditions. Anxiety has myriad forms and shows itself in many different ways. It can involve anxious thoughts (worries, obsessions, ruminations), emotional problems (tension, depressed mood) and physical symptoms (perspiration, heart racing, hands trembling, poor sleep). Each person tends to have their own combination of these symptoms, which can change over time.

You might think that addressing the anxiety provoked by coronavirus would be similar to treating established anxiety disorders and, in some ways, it is. The feelings of anxiety are similar in many of these conditions, even if the triggers and patterns are different. And the broad approach to care is similar in many respects for most disorders that are associated with anxiety.

But, in certain other ways, the anxiety associated with coronavirus is quite different to the anxiety seen in traditional anxiety disorders. Take the example of a person with agoraphobia, a well-recognised anxiety disorder in which the person experiences severe anxiety in an environment that they perceive to be unsafe with no easy way to escape. This condition manifests quite commonly as a paralysing fear of crowded places, so that a person might experience overwhelming anxiety in a supermarket and feel they have to leave. As part of treatment, a psychotherapist can, over the course of months, guide the person to go progressively nearer to a supermarket, then to enter one, and then to remain there for five minutes, ten minutes and eventually longer. Slowly the person will become accustomed to being in the supermarket and realise that there was nothing to fear apart from the anxiety itself.

This approach works well with many anxiety disorders, such as agoraphobia, social phobia and various others. But the key to treating these conditions is that, in all of these disorders, treatment helps the person to see that their anxiety has no basis. There is nothing to fear.

The problem with the anxiety associated with coronavirus is that there is indeed something to fear: the virus. There is nothing good about coronavirus. While the illness is generally mild, with over 97 per cent of people who are diagnosed surviving the infection, that is no consolation if you are one of the few who develops a severe illness or if you fear for a relative who is vulnerable, elderly or ill. Clearly, there is plenty to fear with coronavirus.

And that is what makes the anxiety associated with coronavirus so ubiquitous, so persistent and – to an extent – so challenging to manage. This obstacle is not, however, insurmountable once we bear in mind that traditional techniques for managing anxiety simply need to be adapted to the new situation. Our task today is not to teach ourselves that there is nothing to fear – clearly, there is – but rather to teach ourselves how to keep our anxiety proportionate to the risk, how to live with a certain amount of worry, and how to navigate the uncertainty that coronavirus has brought to our broader lives.

Some people might respond to this situation with denial and apparent indifference. They might ignore public health warnings. This, too, is psychologically understandable, but it is very unhelpful and clearly dangerous. A realistic appraisal of the risks we face and proportionate, considerate and responsible behaviour are what we need – not denial, not complacency, not panic.

The good news is that, just as we are capable of finding sophisticated ways to make ourselves more anxious, we are equally good at finding sophisticated ways to manage our anxieties, once we put our minds to it. Established anxiety-management techniques help greatly once they are modified to suit the new situation that we face.

That is what this book is about.

HOW DID WE GET HERE?

Wuhan is a city of 11 million people in Hubei province in China. It is a city of some significance. On two occasions, in 1927 and 1937, Wuhan served briefly as the capital of China, and it is near to the famous Three Gorges Dam, a power plant and popular tourist attraction. The city is an established centre for finance, education, culture and transport, leading some to call it 'the Chicago of China'. It is now infamous as the centre of the current outbreak of coronavirus.

In late December 2019, a patient in Wuhan Jinyintan Hospital was diagnosed with pneumonia, a severe infection of the lungs. Pneumonia is a very common condition, but this case was different. In this patient, the illness seemed to be caused by a novel virus, i.e. a certain type of transmissible infective agent that was new to humans. Following rapid genetic testing, the new virus was found to most closely resemble a particular virus that was previously found in bats. The virus was characterised as a new 'coronavirus' and named 'COVID-19'.

The novel virus spread rapidly in China. By 20 February 2020, there were over 75,000 cases reported in the country. The age of those infected was usually around 51 years but ranged from just two days to 100 years old. Over three-quarters of cases were aged between 30 and 69 years. Just over half were male.

Over the following months, the new coronavirus spread around the world, well beyond the Chinese border. There was a particular cluster of cases in northern Italy, from which the virus spread rapidly onwards again. By early March 2020, most of the world was experiencing blanket media coverage about coronavirus, how it spreads and – to a lesser extent – what can be done to prevent transmission. By the middle of March, over 170,000 people were infected across 158 countries. More than 6,600 had died. The World Health Organization (WHO) declared a pandemic.

Throughout this period, WHO's official website (www.who.int) has consistently provided comprehensive, accurate and up-to-date information about the outbreak. It is now clear that the disease spreads from person to person through small droplets that come from the nose or mouth when someone with coronavirus coughs or breathes out. The droplets land on surfaces and objects around the person. Transmission occurs when other people touch those surfaces and objects, and then touch their own eyes, nose or mouth. People can also breathe in the droplets, so the WHO advises staying more than 1 metre (3 feet) away from anyone who is coughing or sneezing.

The symptoms of the condition are quite non-specific: fever (high temperature), tiredness and dry cough. There may also be aches and pains, nasal congestion, a runny nose, sore throat or diarrhoea. These symptoms are usually unpleasant but mild, in that they resolve on their own. Approximately 80 per cent of people get better without needing special treatment, but approximately one person in every six will become seriously ill, often with difficulty breathing. This progression is more common among older people and those with pre-existing medical problems such as hypertension (high blood pressure), heart problems or diabetes. People with relevant symptoms should seek medical attention at once, in line with local or national guidelines (see the section on 'What to do if you think you have coronavirus' at the start of this book).

Antibiotics are ineffective against viruses, so treatment of coronavirus is supportive. This means that the symptoms of the virus can be treated and interventions such as oxygen therapy can be used while the person's own body fights the virus. In extreme cases, life support is needed – generally in the intensive care unit of a hospital.

The mortality rate with coronavirus is under 3 per cent of those diagnosed and might be under 1 per cent (as not all those with the infection are diagnosed). In other words, over 97 per cent of people diagnosed with coronavirus will survive it and around 80 per cent will have a mild illness (which probably will not require hospitalisation). For comparison, there was an outbreak of severe acute respiratory syndrome (SARS), a somewhat similar virus, between 2002 and 2003, and that had a mortality rate of 10 per cent but spread less widely. Clearly, however, the current coronavirus pandemic is a public health emergency of the highest order and we must all help to bring it to an end.

Prevention is key. Ireland's Health Service Executive (HSE) recommends a series of simple but highly effective measures to protect yourself and others from transmission of the virus: washing your hands properly and often; covering your mouth and nose with a tissue or your sleeve when you cough and sneeze; putting used tissues into a bin and washing your hands; cleaning and disinfecting frequently touched objects and surfaces; avoiding close contact with people; avoiding crowded places, especially indoors; and following official travel advice, in particular concerning travel to affected areas. Try to avoid touching your face.

It is also important to stay at home if you are sick in order to help stop the spread of any infection you may have. In many countries, these hygiene practices are supplemented by the isolation of newly diagnosed cases, prompt contact-tracing by the authorities, self-isolation, self-quarantine and 'social distancing' aimed at preventing community transmission.

The recommended hygiene measures sound very simple but they are highly effective in preventing the spread of the virus. It is no exaggeration to say that washing our hands and observing good hygiene can save lives – both our own lives and those of other people. Each day, newspapers and websites are filled with pictures of people wearing often unnecessary face masks on our city streets. If all of these images were replaced by pictures of people washing their hands, the message about hand hygiene might reach more people around the world. This message is both simple and life-saving. It bears infinite repeating.

So, two facts are now clear. The first fact is that there is good reason to be worried about coronavirus. It is a new, unfamiliar virus, and some people diagnosed with it will die from it. Many others will become ill, sometimes for several weeks. While the illness is generally mild, it still causes significant suffering and disruptions to personal and family life, as well as broader problems for communities, societies and economies more generally.

The second fact is that simple behaviours focused on good personal hygiene make an enormous difference to the risk of catching or spreading coronavirus. As a result, there is neither reason nor benefit in excessive anxiety or hysteria. Even so, panic and worst-case thinking have gripped the world. This has gone well beyond the point of prompting awareness and good hygiene and is starting to impair reasoned responses to the outbreak. Therefore, in addition to the public health measures recommended by the WHO and others, there are several psychological measures that can help us to manage the panic that has engulfed the planet and our own excessive personal anxieties about the outbreak.

HOW THIS BOOK WORKS

This book presents a psychological toolkit for the management of anxiety and panic related to coronavirus. The book aims to assist readers to recognise the legitimate risks presented by coronavirus, place that risk in context and in proportion, and diminish the unnecessary, disabling panic that many people feel. We have more power than we think.

Chapter 1 is titled 'Knowing' and emphasises the importance of staying informed about coronavirus but not obsessing about it, not filling in knowledge gaps with speculation or random musings from social media, and – most importantly – limiting the time you spend each day consuming information about the outbreak (15 minutes twice per day is plenty). More broadly, this chapter recommends taking time to get to know your 'information habits' better and becoming more familiar with how your emotional life actually works. This can be a surprising exercise for many people, and it will help us navigate current and future challenges with greater self-awareness.

Chapter 2 is titled 'Thinking' and explores the importance of thinking clearly about coronavirus while avoiding the common errors that routinely lead us astray and fuel a sense of anxiety and hysteria. In particular, it is important that we focus on what we can control in this situation (especially when explaining coronavirus to children) and that we avoid unhelpful thinking habits such as negative automatic thoughts, over-generalisation, personalisation and negative filtering. Simple exercises such as thought-labelling can help us to consciously recognise irrational thoughts and label them as such in our heads. It is also useful to actively think about the problems that others face, because we gain a deeper perspective when we see ourselves as part of a larger whole.

Chapter 3 moves on to look at 'Feeling' and recommends becoming more aware of our emotions and labelling them clearly as emotions rather than thoughts, in order to recognise their power. It is important to remember that emotions can disguise themselves as behaviours or facts and can therefore mislead us, especially when the world is filled with free-floating anxiety about the current outbreak of coronavirus. Talking to others about our feelings is central to the cultivation of honest, direct awareness. Listening is just as important as speaking. If you want to be heard, listen.

Chapter 4 centres on 'Doing' what we can to assist with our psychological response to coronavirus, and avoiding behaviour we shouldn't engage in. It is important that we do things that help, such as following public health advice, and refrain from activities that increase panic without delivering any benefit. It is also useful to focus on activities that are not directly related to coronavirus but are vital for our physical and mental wellbeing: maintaining a healthy diet, exercising, prioritising good sleep, spending time outdoors and finding an activity that absorbs us and clears other worries from our minds (if only for defined periods). We should reward ourselves for achievements (however small) and consciously practise compassion towards ourselves and others. There is no 'me' with a problem like coronavirus; there is only 'us'. All health is public health. We can only manage this together.

Chapter 5 explores the idea of 'Being' as opposed to 'Doing', on the basis that we are 'human beings' rather than 'human doings'. Coronavirus presents real challenges to how we see ourselves and how we understand the world around us, which suddenly seems more fragile and threatening than before. But there are ways to navigate this anxiety, once we retain a sense of proportion, try not to project other unrelated life problems onto our anxiety about coronavirus, and rediscover the profound value that lies in solidarity with each other, especially at times like this.

The book concludes with a summary of the advice provided and suggestions for ways to move forward, balancing the problems of today with the possibilities of tomorrow. Working together is key. People quarantined at home in China and Italy sing together out their windows. We need more of that.

1
KNOWING

The world is awash with information, advice, speculation, rumours and falsehoods about coronavirus. Some of the material is useful and reliable, such as the facts and advice provided on the websites of the WHO (www.who.int), the United States' Centers for Disease Control and Prevention (CDC) (www.cdc.gov), the United Kingdom's National Health Service (NHS) (www.nhs.uk) and Ireland's Health Service Executive (HSE) (www.hse.ie). Reputable medical journals such as *The Lancet* (www.thelancet.com) and *BMJ* (www.bmj.com) have made extensive information and breaking research freely available to health professionals and the public. There are a lot of reliable resources out there.

The problem is that much of this good information is being swept away by oceans of misleading, uninformed and false information, especially on social media. Therefore, while it is very important to stay informed about coronavirus, it is equally important to curate your sources of information with care and to prioritise reliable sources. To this end, the three suggestions in this chapter focus on 'knowing' what we need to know about coronavirus and limiting the impact of false, misleading and exaggerated information.

DO STAY INFORMED ABOUT CORONAVIRUS
(BUT DO NOT OBSESS)

First, stay informed about coronavirus but do not obsess about it. While coronavirus is certainly very bad news (there is absolutely nothing good about it), we amplify its negative psychological effects if we obsess over the repetitive media coverage and consume every single update from every single country every single day. While it is good to stay informed, it is not necessary to read about each case as it is diagnosed in each country around the world. Enough is enough.

Social media is especially pernicious because so much of it is driven not by facts but by emotion, bias, prejudice and lies. This is regrettable. Social media can do much good by providing rapid information and facilitating supportive networks. But in times of panic, the negatives most commonly outweigh the positives, unless we take active steps to limit our consumption, think critically about what we read, and refrain from amplifying false or misleading information within our own social networks.

So, that is the first piece of advice in this psychological toolkit: limit your media intake about coronavirus to certain periods of the day and only use sources you can trust, such as those listed in the 'Further information' at the end of this book. Restrict your media consumption about the pandemic to two 15-minute periods each day, one in the morning and one in the evening. Try to ignore everything else about coronavirus for the rest of the day, unless it directly concerns you, your family or your work. Tune in to the global situation twice daily only. Set a media limit for each day and stick to it, no matter what.

DON'T FILL IN KNOWLEDGE GAPS WITH SPECULATION OR RANDOM MUSINGS ON SOCIAL MEDIA (THERE ARE SOME THINGS WE SIMPLY DO NOT KNOW)

Coronavirus is not fully understood. The gaps in our knowledge are being researched all the time, but results are slow to come in. As a consequence, we need to live with a certain level of uncertainty about the virus and the illness that it causes. There is, however, a tendency to fill these information gaps with speculation and guesses, many of which are presented as facts.

False information has two negative effects. First, some people might believe the falsehoods, share them with other people, and spread misinformation, possibly unwittingly. This problem can be addressed by focusing on information sources that you trust, asking yourself if what you read seems reasonable, exercising critical thought about all the information you come across, and thinking twice before repeating information to other people, especially if you are uncertain about it. This approach might be described as 'information mindfulness' – maintaining a keen awareness of what you are reading and what it really means. This should also protect against the tendency among some people to compulsively read negative information and therefore stoke their own anxiety.

The second problem with false information is a much more insidious one. It stems from the fact that, even if we don't believe what we read, the information still has an effect on us emotionally or subconsciously. In other words, even if our logical brain dismisses some information as false, that information can still have an emotional effect of which we might be unaware. Over time, these small emotional effects can silently accumulate even if our logical brain dismisses the anxiety-provoking information every time we read it. In the end, this anxiety emerges one way or another in our lives, in the form of anxiety attacks, panic disorder or even depression.

This problem can be addressed by not only limiting our media intake to certain times of the day and restricting ourselves to trusted sources, but also 'reality-testing' all information as soon as we read it and developing enhanced emotional awareness about how our media consumption affects our moods. For example, if you ever feel generally anxious without knowing precisely why, it is good to review both what you did and what media you consumed during the day. Perhaps your media consumption is silently affecting your mood in ways that you do not notice at the time. It all builds up.

Identifying these kinds of negative patterns is the first step towards changing them. And, as part of this, you should not add to the problem for yourself and others by filling knowledge gaps about coronavirus with speculation or random musings on social media: there are some things that we simply do not know. It bears repeating that, for now, we need to live with a certain amount of uncertainty about coronavirus.

DO TRY TO KNOW YOURSELF BETTER (THIS WILL HELP YOU NAVIGATE THE CHALLENGES MORE MINDFULLY AND WITH GREATER SELF-AWARENESS)

We spend an increasing proportion of our lives online and, for many, social media occupies a great deal of that time. Despite these trends, most of us have little conscious awareness, if any, of what our information habits are: which pieces of information we believe, which sources we go to for amusement rather than knowledge, and the effect that all of this has on our inner lives. This is a real pity.

Gaining self-knowledge is one of the key steps towards achieving deeper happiness. As a result, most of us need to develop a greater awareness of both the stresses in our lives and the simple steps that we can take to reduce them. On the other side of the equation, it is also useful to consciously list out the activities that we enjoy and that make us happy, and see can we find more space for these in our lives. These are two of the key habits for happiness: consciously and deliberately identifying stresses and managing them as best as possible, and identifying things that make us happy and optimising them as much as is feasible.

Building these habits for happiness helps us to cope better when exceptional stresses enter our lives, such as serious illness, personal loss and the uncertainties associated with coronavirus. By reflecting on our lives with greater focus, and possibly discussing these issues with friends, we can identify patterns and habits that we may need to change. Such change can be dramatic or incremental. In relation to social media, for example, there is a compelling argument to delete all your social media accounts in one fell swoop. Alternatively, you could aim to limit your use in other ways or reduce your screen-time by 10 per cent each week for four or five weeks and see how you get on. Small steps have big effects. Drama is rarely necessary and seldom sustainable.

There are also many other areas in our lives that we can change in order to strengthen our habits for happiness, in addition to reflecting on what truly stresses us and what makes us happy. In the current climate of anxiety and panic about coronavirus, however, it is especially important that we prioritise trying to know ourselves better and understanding how our emotional lives actually work. In ancient Greece, this advice was summarised in two words: 'Know thyself'. Heeding that suggestion will help us to navigate the challenges we face with greater mindfulness, self-awareness and resilience.

2
THINKING

Hamlet, in Act II of Shakespeare's play, argues that 'there is nothing either good or bad, but thinking makes it so'. Hamlet was both wrong and right. He was wrong because some things, like coronavirus, are just bad. But Hamlet was right in suggesting that our thinking patterns have an enormous effect on what we believe, how we behave and how we feel. This is never more relevant than during a period of acute anxiety, as is the case with coronavirus at present. Left to their own devices at a time like this, our thoughts will literally run away with themselves and move us ever closer to panic, despite the logical parts of our brains knowing that panic is deeply counter-productive.

Luckily, there are several techniques that we can use to help keep our thoughts more rational and centred on reality. Many of these techniques focus on developing an awareness of the unhelpful thinking habits that so frequently affect our thoughts and distort our perceptions of reality. To this end, the three suggestions in this chapter focus on the importance of 'thinking' clearly about coronavirus and avoiding the common pitfalls or thinking errors that so often lead us astray and fuel a sense of anxiety and panic.

DO FOCUS ON WHAT YOU CAN CONTROL IN THIS SITUATION (ESPECIALLY WHEN EXPLAINING CORONAVIRUS TO CHILDREN)

At the best of times, it is easy to feel overwhelmed. There is even comfort in admitting defeat because it feels like such an admission excuses us from taking action, at least for now. If our problems are too big to be solved, why should we bother doing anything at all? Is there any point in trying?

This remarkably unhelpful psychological manoeuvre results in very short-lived consolation without helping in any way to solve the problems that we face. The key to avoiding this reaction is to differentiate between the overall problem at its highest level and the actions that we can take in our personal lives, which often seem very small in the context of the bigger picture. But that is no reason to step back and give up entirely. It is useful to think of the well-known environmental slogan, 'Think global, act local'. Small actions matter greatly, both in the bigger picture and in our own lives.

In the case of coronavirus, this means acknowledging the extent of the global problem, but then focusing on what we can do in our daily lives to assist with addressing it: staying informed, following WHO guidelines about hygiene and avoiding transmission, and seeking to carry on with the other parts of our lives as best as possible.

This down-to-earth, pragmatic approach is particularly important with children, who pick up on the hysterical tone of media coverage and often ask very direct questions, especially about older relatives who might be at increased risk. Children can express stress through changes in eating or sleeping behaviour, the return of habits from earlier in childhood, general irritation or avoidance of school or other activities.

The best approach is to tell children that there is a problem with a new illness, but that simple things like washing our hands with greater care can help everyone to stay well. Children need reassurance that they are safe. Like adults, they derive great comfort from structure in their day. Children also imitate their parents, so be sure to limit your media consumption, take plenty of exercise and try to maintain the rhythms of daily life as best as possible. When discussing coronavirus, the key is to translate big concepts, which have infinite capacity to overwhelm us, into concrete actions which can both reduce risk and demonstrate the elements of this situation that we can control.

The fact that our individual actions might seem small does not matter. If everyone took these simple steps, such as improving their personal hygiene, the global effect would be enormous. Inaction is the worst of all possible worlds. Edmund Burke, an eighteenth-century Irish statesman and philosopher, wrote that 'nobody made a greater mistake than he who did nothing because he could do only a little'. With coronavirus, little actions by millions can literally save lives.

DON'T FALL INTO UNHELPFUL THINKING HABITS (AUDIT YOUR THOUGHTS)

Cognitive-behavioural therapy for anxiety disorders and various other psychological conditions has identified specific thinking habits that distort our view of reality and contribute to unnecessary anxiety. This therapy focuses on recognising these errors, reducing their incidence and developing alternative thought patterns. Auditing your thoughts for these errors and being more aware of them can help stem the panic that is now so commonly associated with coronavirus.

The first of these errors is 'catastrophisation', which is an irrational tendency to believe, and behave as if, a given problem is far worse than it really is. Applying this concept in the present situation is complex because coronavirus really is a catastrophe for many people affected by it. But there is a crucial difference between recognising that something is catastrophic and allowing that realisation to paralyse our thoughts and behaviour. In the case of coronavirus, rational appraisal of the enormous problems it presents should not catastrophise all of us into paralysis. An awareness of this distinction is vital: we can recognise that something is catastrophic, but we should still rationally assess the size and nature of the challenge, and take action based on that. Catastrophisation and paralysis help nobody, least of all ourselves.

The second cognitive error likely to prove especially unhelpful in our present context is 'negative automatic thoughts'. These are negative thoughts that we relate to ourselves in disproportionate and irrational ways. They often involve over-generalisation. An example is: 'Work did not go well today so I am clearly incapable of doing my job.' Or: 'I forgot to wash my hands properly and therefore I am a useless person.' Or: 'People are having difficulty controlling coronavirus, so, if I catch it, I will certainly pass it on to everyone I know.'

Even if you dismiss these thoughts seconds after you

think them, having these kinds of negative thoughts repeatedly throughout the day will still have an effect on your mood. Other examples include presuming that things are your fault when they are not, or presuming that you will be unable to assist others if called upon. Recognising negative automatic thoughts helps greatly with preventing them and minimising their impact in our lives.

'Personalisation' is another common cognitive error. An example is: 'The event did not go well, most likely because I arrived five minutes late. It is all my fault'. This degree of self-reference can cause problems in relation to coronavirus, most notably if, for example, you read about a case of coronavirus and immediately assume that this will happen to you too. 'Negative filtering' is another unhelpful habit, as we tend to ignore information that does not accord with our opinions and concentrate on information that supports our pre-existing negative outlook.

To address these unhelpful thinking habits, it is useful, in the first instance, to have an awareness that these tendencies are common features of our thoughts. Second, simple exercises such as thought-labelling can help greatly, focusing on consciously recognising irrational thoughts and labelling them as such in our heads. This reduces their occurrence and helps minimise their effect on our mood.

DO THINK OF OTHERS (WE GAIN PERSPECTIVE WHEN WE SEE OURSELVES AS PART OF A LARGER WHOLE)

When faced with an event like the current pandemic, it is important to remain compassionate towards ourselves (we are doing our best) and others (so are they). It is especially important that we continue to see ourselves as part of a larger whole, as one element in our common humanity. This can be a difficult task, so it is useful to make a conscious effort to think about other people, especially in poor and developing countries, as the outbreak of coronavirus continues around the world.

The early spread of the virus outside China clearly tracked flight paths, chiefly to rich countries. Despite the substantial problems that the virus presents in these countries, rich countries are still better placed to contain potential outbreaks: better sanitation, better nutrition, better healthcare. The picture will be very different in developing countries. They need enormous support. If those of us who live in rich countries can shift some of the focus from ourselves and on to others, everyone will be better off.

The Buddhist idea of 'no self' is very useful here. In essence, Buddhism teaches that everything we experience, including the 'self', exists because of specific circumstances, causes and conditions. These circumstances can change very rapidly, as we have seen with the sudden arrival of coronavirus. As a result, it is clear that everything is dependent on everything else and that my idea of my 'self' is far less permanent, inviolable or autonomous than it sometimes seems to be. Humans are an intrinsically networked phenomena, part of a bigger web of circumstances and conditions that are constantly in motion and continually in a state of change.

As a result, we need to bear in mind that each of us is an embedded part of something bigger than any one of us. All humans are deeply connected with each other, almost to the point that the entire human race could be usefully considered to be a single living organism. The spread of coronavirus and the panic associated with it demonstrates just how true this is. And this is a powerful argument in favour of compassion towards all sentient beings, including ourselves. The suffering of other people is continuous with our suffering – just as their happiness is continuous with ours.

Based on this perspective, perhaps the first step we should take is to ensure that we do not harm others, in line with one of the oldest principles of medicine: *'primum non nocere'* or 'first, do no harm'. In the context of the coronavirus pandemic, this means following public health advice and thinking before we speak about the virus. Casual speculation can spread harmful myths, amplify our own thinking errors and fuel panic in other people and ourselves. We need to talk about the virus, but we should not risk spreading falsehoods unwittingly or exaggerating various aspects of the issue.

It is also useful to focus on feeling kindness and compassion for all who suffer and for ourselves. There is a very useful Buddhist meditation practice that focuses on these skills, called 'loving kindness meditation'. This involves finding a quiet spot where you can sit in a comfortable, upright position for 10 or 15 minutes. To begin, gather your thoughts and try to dispel the events of the day. Then, try to feel loving kindness for yourself. This is not easy to summon up at will, but if your thoughts wander, gently bring them back into focus. Try to feel a sense of kindness towards yourself.

Next, try to feel loving kindness for someone for whom it is easy to feel loving kindness (e.g. a friend), then for someone neutral (e.g. a stranger) and then for someone for whom you find it difficult to feel loving kindness. Finish the practice by reflecting on the need for loving kindness for the entire world and everyone in it. It is easy to get distracted from this task, but do stick with it, gently re-focusing your thoughts when they wander.

This exercise helps us to practise feeling compassion towards ourselves and others, and it reminds us of the need to think about other people, especially those who suffer. Clearly, this is particularly important at the present time. Coronavirus is a global problem and we gain perspective when we see ourselves as part of a larger global whole. We are not alone in this – and neither is anyone else. Realising this fact is a deep consolation, and it helps to place world events in the context of our lives, and our lives in the context of world events.

3
FEELING

The Greek philosopher Aristotle reportedly said that a human being is a 'rational animal'. If Aristotle truly said this, then he, like Hamlet in the last chapter, was both right and wrong. Aristotle was right to the extent that humans have enormously complex brains, comprising over 86 billion nerve cells along with many more supporting structures, brain chemicals and various other cells. And, for the most part, we use our brains to good effect: understanding the world, solving problems and communicating with each other in astonishingly subtle ways. Our brains are truly extraordinary.

But Aristotle was wrong if he thought that human beings are entirely rational. There is growing evidence that many of the decisions that we believe to be logical and rational are deeply influenced by emotion and profoundly shaped by irrational beliefs. We are not the logical thinking machines that we sometimes imagine ourselves to be. This means that we need to devote greater attention to emotions in our day-to-day lives, especially at times when feelings run high, such as now, during the current outbreak of coronavirus.

With this in mind, the three suggestions in this chapter focus on 'feelings' with a view to helping us to become more aware of our emotions and recognise when feelings rather than logic are governing our behaviour. There is nothing wrong with emotions shaping what we do, but it is useful to recognise when it is happening and to be more aware of the interplay between logic and emotion in our thoughts and actions.

DO BECOME MORE AWARE OF YOUR EMOTIONS (LABELLING THEM AS EMOTIONS HELPS US TO RECOGNISE THEIR POWER)

The first step is to identify your emotions as you feel them. Clearly labelling each emotion will help you to recognise how you feel and how strong your current emotions really are.

Second, work hard to accept your emotions, regardless of what they are. You cannot negotiate directly with emotions, so you need to accept your anger, your frustration, your fear or your happiness. You should, however, remain confident that you can handle any emotion: these are all transient feelings and they will pass.

Third, try to figure out why you feel this way right now. Is there a trigger? Sometimes there is a clear trigger and sometimes there is not. It is especially useful to identify when negative emotions have no clear focus. This helps them to dissipate.

The coronavirus outbreak has triggered strong emotions in many people. These are commonly centred on anxiety, anger, fear and sadness. It is important to recognise these feelings. It is also important to recognise that coronavirus has placed many people in unfamiliar situations which will provoke unfamiliar emotions. For example, many countries ask people who have symptoms of coronavirus to 'self-isolate'. This means avoiding contact with other people. In some countries, limited social interaction is advised, while general 'social distancing' is in effect in others.

While all of these steps are effective public health measures, they create unusual social and emotional situations with which most people are unfamiliar. Quarantine has similar effects, often resulting in fear of infection, frustration, boredom and annoyance at lack of information. There can also be problems with stigma, finances and tensions in relationships, as well as anger towards people from epicentres of the outbreak and towards governments for perceived inaction.

These problems can be mitigated by public health authorities terminating these measures when they are no longer clinically indicated, providing adequate information and supplies to those affected, improving communication (using technology where possible) and, for children, continuing schooling and education as best as is feasible. Emotional awareness is vital.

These are unusual circumstances at a time of unique emotional intensity. Labelling our emotions and checking in on how we feel can help greatly as we navigate these challenges.

DON'T FORGET THAT EMOTIONS CAN DISGUISE THEMSELVES AS BEHAVIOURS OR FACTS – AND CAN THEREFORE MISLEAD US

The problem with much of the advice about managing our emotions is that our emotions do not always present themselves as emotions. Often, they manifest as behaviours that we poorly understand (even in ourselves), 'facts' that upset us (and likely are not true) or a general sense of confusion about what is going on (and how we are feeling). This is especially true when someone is diagnosed as ill or is asked to do something that suggests that, while they are not yet ill, they might soon be (e.g. self-isolation or limited social interaction). These situations feel midway between wellness and illness. You are well, but you are being treated as if you are ill. So, how, exactly, are you supposed to feel? Well or ill?

The first step in dealing with these peculiar and distressing situations is to recognise that we can have several conflicting emotions at the same time or in quick succession. The rules of logic apply loosely, if at all. Much of what we feel might not make sense, at least at first glance. Recognising this is important. We like to think that our emotions and inner lives have a certain reason to them, but sometimes we need to acknowledge the existence of a tangle of emotions that we simply cannot figure out. There they are. So be it.

The second step in this situation is to practise simply sitting with uncomfortable emotional states – tolerating distress without trying to understand it fully. An activity like meditation helps greatly with this. To try this, find a quiet spot where you are unlikely to be disturbed. You will never find a place that is entirely secluded but do try to find one that minimises disturbances and distractions. Having calmed your body gently and centred your thoughts in the moment, focus on your breath. To begin, silently count ten breaths on the in-breath. Then count ten breaths on the out-breath. Then count ten breaths on the turning of the breath. And then start again.

As you try to do this, a variety of thoughts will inevitably enter your head. Emotions will come to the surface and you will get distracted. The work of meditation lies in observing these thoughts, emotions and distractions but not engaging with them. So, try not to explore these distractions in your head. Simply try to sit with them and observe how quickly such passing thoughts and emotions disappear once we deny them the oxygen of our attention.

This is not easy to achieve, so do not be dismayed if you get distracted. Simply try again. Commit to trying this for ten minutes. Do not berate yourself each time you get distracted. Practise self-compassion. Gently direct your thoughts back to your breathing. This is a skill that takes time. If it does not work out today, try again tomorrow. If it does not work out tomorrow, try the next day. And so on.

Meditation is often described as 'a practice'. This is very true. Even the meditation masters, after decades of contemplation, are still 'practicing'.

DO TALK TO OTHERS ABOUT YOUR FEELINGS (BUT LABEL THEM CLEARLY AS FEELINGS RATHER THAN FACTS)

It is helpful to talk to other people about how you are feeling. It is equally helpful to listen to others who are often experiencing the same emotions as you are but might express them differently. Take time to let them explain. Once you listen properly, you will see how similar we all are.

When expressing your emotions, be sure to label them as feelings rather than facts. It can help to write down how you feel beforehand. It is not helpful for you or others to express feelings through anonymous, hysterical speculation on social media. The Buddhist concept of 'right speech' is relevant here. This is one of the key tenets of the 'Noble Eightfold Path' of Buddhism. It centres on avoiding harsh words against others, only saying what is true, speaking in a way that promotes understanding, using a reasonable tone of voice and ensuring that our speech is honest. This is also known as 'mindful speech'.

It is sometimes difficult to adhere to right speech, particularly when we are upset. But right speech is especially important when we are distressed and at times of threat, illness or personal loss. These issues are clearly relevant in the context of coronavirus. For some people, personal losses might include loss of hope, loss of health and, for others, bereavement. Direct, truthful communication is vital in these circumstances. We need to remember that discussing emotions is central to honest communication. Listening is just as important as speaking.

In other words: if you want to be heard, listen.

4
DOING

'Commission bias' is the term used to describe the human tendency to do things rather than not do things. Faced with a problem, we have an innate desire to act, to intervene, to actively *do* something, even if our actions might be ineffective or even make the situation worse. Despite the risks, we prefer action to inaction, even if the outcome of our actions is uncertain or harmful. This universal tendency to act lies at the root of many human problems. Sometimes, it would be far better if we just sat back, reflected and chose our actions with greater care. In the words of the Buddhist proverb: 'Don't just do something, sit there.'

Against this background, this chapter looks at 'doing' what we can to assist with our psychological response to coronavirus, and avoiding behaviour we shouldn't engage in. Suggestions include following public health advice to minimise risk and reduce virus transmission, doing various things that are not related to coronavirus but help maintain general health (e.g. exercise), consciously practicing compassion for ourselves and others, and rewarding ourselves for our achievements (which is especially important during times of ubiquitous anxiety). Equally important, this chapter looks at what we should *not* do, so that we do not act in ways that might inadvertently harm or disadvantage others, let alone ourselves.

DO NOT DO THINGS THAT INCREASE PANIC WITHOUT DELIVERING ANY BENEFIT

The WHO and national health authorities have clear, evolving guidelines about public health measures designed to address coronavirus. Follow these guidelines. The WHO knows what it is doing. Even if you feel that the advice does not apply to you, it does. Many of the recommendations are population-based measures that only achieve their goals if everyone follows them. Do as advised. And if the advice changes, follow the new advice. This is a changing situation.

Many of us have a desire to do more than is advised. This is not always helpful. Take the issue of face masks. At the time of writing, the WHO states that people with no respiratory symptoms do not need face masks. Face masks are recommended for people who have symptoms of coronavirus and people caring for those who display symptoms, such as a cough and fever. This includes healthcare workers and people who are minding someone either in a healthcare facility or at home. At the present time, there is no reason for people outside of these categories to wear face masks.

In fact, not only is it usually unnecessary and pointless for people outside of these categories to wear face masks on city streets, it actually causes two major problems. First, if face masks are worn by millions of people who do not need them, there will be a shortage of face masks for the sick and for healthcare workers who genuinely need them. There are already shortages of face masks in many countries, despite major boosts to production. This increases risk for everyone and will prolong the pandemic.

The second problem with unnecessary face masks is that they fuel panic in the general population. People wearing face masks automatically trigger anxiety, in themselves as much as anyone else. Face masks give visual form to the psychological barrier between 'us' (the well) and 'them' (the ill). If the general wearing of masks served a medical purpose, this might be a reasonable price to pay. But unnecessary masks on city streets simply deepen this division with no benefit. They cast the entire world into the category of the 'ill', even though most people do not have coronavirus.

By wearing unnecessary face masks, we are harming the global response to coronavirus, isolating ourselves and fuelling panic in others. And panic is the only thing that spreads even faster than a virus. The best advice is not to wear a face mask unless the WHO, your national health authority or your doctors advise you to do so.

DO OTHER THINGS (EAT, SLEEP, EXERCISE, GO OUTSIDE IF YOU CAN)

It is easy to become obsessed by coronavirus and the blanket media coverage that it commands. It is also easy to become downhearted by the effect of coronavirus on the world, the loneliness of 'social distancing' and the uncertainties of our new situation, along with personal illnesses, losses or bereavements. In these circumstances, it is more important than ever that we prioritise our physical and mental wellbeing in order to both minimise the effect of coronavirus on us and maintain our mental health.

Both physical and mental wellbeing matter. We are embodied creatures: our heads are firmly connected to our bodies, so there is no real distinction between physical and mental health. In our present circumstance, we need to pay particular attention to both by watching our diet, exercising and making sure we sleep as best as possible. Going outside (on our own if necessary) and connecting with others (using technology if required) can be especially helpful, insofar as they are possible.

First, try your best to keep some kind of exercise regime going, no matter what. The best time to exercise is in the morning. Each week, the average adult should get 150 minutes of moderate aerobic activity (e.g.

brisk walking or mowing the lawn) or 75 minutes of vigorous aerobic activity (e.g. running). We should also do strength exercises on two or more days, working all of our major muscles (legs, hips, back, abdomen, chest, shoulders and arms). If your favourite gym is not accessible, go outdoors if possible. Often, just going outside is the best way to interrupt negative thought spirals and become immersed in the world immediately around you. It is not always possible to 'think your way' out of anxiety. Sometimes, we need to close the laptop, stand up, leave the phone behind and just go outside.

Second, take some time to ensure that you get enough sleep. Adults should ideally have 7 to 9 hours of sleep in every 24 hours. Newborns need 14 to 17 hours of sleep; pre-schoolers need 10 to 13 hours; school-aged children need 9 to 11 hours; and teenagers need 8 to 10 hours. Very few of us meet these requirements. There are many ways to optimise our sleep habits and prioritising these methods is especially important at times of heightened anxiety or stress.

Bedrooms should be dark, cool (around 16–18°C), quiet, uncluttered and free of gadgets (such as televisions and phones). The bed should be comfortable, with a new mattress every eight to ten years. In the evening, reduce the intensity of light (using dimmer switches or low wattage bulbs); establish a bedtime routine and regular sleep pattern; avoid alcohol and sugar; try not to nap during the day; and do not use computers, mobile phones or televisions before trying to sleep. Breathing exercises or counting sheep can help you to fall asleep. If you wake at night, follow the '20-minute rule': if you cannot sleep for 20 minutes, read a (printed) book for 20 minutes and then try to sleep. If that does not work, repeat the procedure until you eventually fall asleep. Avoid alcohol, tea, coffee and screens if you are awake at night.

In addition to paying attention to diet, exercise and sleep, it is also important that coronavirus does not overshadow any other health problems that you may have or may develop. Be sure to contact your general practitioner if you have any physical illnesses or feel you are developing a mental illness, such as depression. Maintaining general health is vital during an outbreak such as the present one.

Finally, one of the best ways to maintain mental health is to find an activity that absorbs you and clears all other worries from your mind for a period of time. For many people, running provides this kind of complete absorption in the present moment. They simply lose themselves in the activity. This can also occur with jigsaws, puzzles, card games, reading, music, playing with children or spending time with a pet. For others, yoga or meditation can meet this need, and both activities can be practised alone (if self-isolating), in virtual groups (using technology) or within small groups of friends, depending on your circumstances. Whatever way you achieve it, try to spend time in a state of absorption or a state of 'flow' while you do some activity that you enjoy and that makes the rest of the world melt away. This refreshes your mental state and leaves you better placed to face any challenges that lie ahead.

DO REWARD YOURSELF FOR YOUR ACHIEVEMENTS AND CONSCIOUSLY PRACTISE COMPASSION FOR YOURSELF AND OTHERS

During a pandemic, it is easy to become despondent. However, while we must acknowledge the realities of loss and bereavement, we must also find a way to carry on. Many of us have other people who rely on us: children, family members with disabilities, neighbours with illnesses and so forth. Balancing sadness with hope is difficult. The best approach is to acknowledge the broader realities of our situation but not be paralysed by them in our own lives. Focus on daily activities and short-terms plans.

Above all, be compassionate towards yourself and others. Everyone is worried and each person expresses this differently. Some people express anxiety through extreme irritation and unpleasantness. Tolerating this can be difficult, but it is a good exercise in compassion if we try to understand that the other person feels the same as we do, deep down.

We should also be compassionate towards ourselves. Reward yourself for getting through the day, for exercising, for helping others, for trying to balance all of your concerns and for simply keeping going. Some days, that alone is a considerable task and it deserves recognition.

Depending on the extent to which you are directly affected, try not to let coronavirus become the one and only theme in your life. If your circumstances permit, make a conscious effort to think broadly about the world. Use your worry about coronavirus to help with this task. For example, many people have cancelled unnecessary air travel as a result of the virus. This is, at least, good for the planet. Indeed, if even 10 per cent of the unproductive panic about coronavirus was shifted to climate change, the world would be a substantially better place and our response to coronavirus would be none the weaker.

5
BEING

It is commonly said that we are 'human beings', not 'human doings'. But while this is a catchy slogan, what does it actually mean? Does it mean anything? And how does it connect with the challenges that we currently face with coronavirus?

On the face of it, the message seems simple. We all get caught up in the problems of each day: things to do, places to be, people to meet. This is understandable. But if we reduce our lives to lists of tasks or places to go, we miss out on a great deal of what it means to be human. We were designed to live in the world, not simply to move through it. Too often, each day is just a lengthy 'to do' list. A good day is when we get everything ticked off the list. And then we go to bed.

But, from time to time, something comes along that stops us in our tracks, disrupts our busy lives and – quite possibly – forces us to think again about what it means to be a human being and not just a doer of tasks. For many people, coronavirus has prompted just such thoughts. Does this pandemic mean that we are more physically and psychologically fragile than we thought? Has the outbreak indelibly changed the way we see ourselves and our place in the world? Has it altered our way of life forever? Does it signal the end of globalisation?

The previous four chapters of this book have focused on 'Knowing', 'Thinking', 'Feeling' and 'Doing'. This chapter focuses on 'Being' and how the coronavirus outbreak might or might not change the way we view ourselves as human beings. This chapter covers issues such as keeping all of this in proportion (more things will stay the same than will change), not projecting unrelated life problems onto our anxiety about coronavirus (which only amplifies our worries) and rediscovering the profound value that lies in solidarity with other humans (especially at times of high anxiety). This is a chapter about simply 'being'.

DO REMEMBER THAT *PROPORTIONALITY* IS THE KEY

Anxiety and panic can seem infinite, but nothing is truly infinite. While risk always exists, it has limits and it changes constantly. As a result, neither complacency nor panic is appropriate, even when faced with a challenge like coronavirus. Proportionate, mindful engagement is key. As humans, we have great difficulty keeping things in perspective and making our worries proportionate to their root causes. We need to work on this if we are to stop seeing coronavirus as an existential threat and start seeing it as a serious public health problem that needs to be solved.

Buddhist tradition places strong emphasis on 'seeing things as they really are' and not as our worried brains imagine them to be. Ultimately, this task centres on the eternal conflict between logic and emotion in the human mind. The WHO, in its advice about mental health during the coronavirus outbreak, is logical, pragmatic and proportionate. The WHO advises limiting media consumption, protecting yourself, assisting others and acknowledging the positive work of so many people in response to the virus. Healthcare workers need to pay particular attention to their physical and mental health and their own stress levels.

The WHO guidance emphasises logical, day-to-day steps that we can take to mitigate the risks presented by coronavirus rather than letting our emotional brains distress us disproportionately or paralyse us completely. It is good advice. We should follow it.

But the WHO's careful, consistent repetition of public health messages also serves several more profound psychological purposes by implicitly stating that we have considerable power over the spread of coronavirus, that there are organisations that know what to do, and that, regardless of the changing face of the outbreak, much of the advice remains constant: maintain good personal hygiene, rapidly respond to cases once identified and take steps to reduce transmission. While we cannot and should not ignore our emotions, we need to respond to them proportionately and always leave room for logic, pragmatism and action. As the WHO implies, the coronavirus pandemic demands no less.

DO NOT PROJECT OTHER LIFE PROBLEMS ONTO YOUR ANXIETY ABOUT CORONAVIRUS

The second point to make in relation to 'being' concerns people who are not ill with coronavirus and do not have a family member affected by it, but who are still profoundly, psychologically disturbed by the outbreak. For such people, it is important to remember that while coronavirus is a serious problem that we need to manage, anxiety about the virus does not completely define them as people. It is tempting to project all kinds of coincidental life problems onto this anxiety and to imagine that everything was perfect before the virus came and that everything will be perfect again after the outbreak has subsided. While this is an understandable psychological response, it is unrealistic, especially among those not directly affected, and it does not help us either now or in the long term.

It is certainly true that an event such as a pandemic or global health crisis can and should make us more grateful for the good things in our lives, and that this enhanced sense of gratitude might persist after the outbreak. But this does not mean that people who are not directly affected should think themselves into a state where they identify coronavirus as the one and only issue in their lives. In order to prevent this occurring, we should not endlessly focus on our anxious thoughts about the outbreak but, rather, divert some of that energy away from our brains and towards simple physical activities that are proven to relieve stress.

The Substance Abuse and Mental Health Services Administration in the US, in their guidance on coping with stress during outbreaks of infectious diseases, advise us to note signs of stress in our behaviour, our bodies, our emotions and our thinking. They identify many ways to relieve stress, several of which are based on moving away from our thoughts and focusing on behaviours such as having a good diet, exercising, resting, avoiding too much caffeine and alcohol, and avoiding tobacco and illegal drugs completely. Find time to pursue your hobbies, have a good meal, take a bath and connect with others, they suggest.

This approach does not mean avoiding the issues at hand. Quite the opposite: it means staying informed, keeping things in perspective and taking care of ourselves. Above all, it means spending less time reading ill-informed rumours, less time ruminating on our own anxieties and less time projecting our other life problems onto our anxiety about coronavirus. It means spending more time focusing on facts, more time following simple public health advice and more time engaging in activities that prioritise physical actions that help us rather than endless worries that don't. We are always bigger than our anxiety.

DO FIND TIME TO REDISCOVER THE VALUE OF BEING WITH OTHER PEOPLE

Most of us harbour secret worries. Perhaps, at some level, we know that these anxieties are illogical or exaggerated, but, yet, we worry. That is the very essence of anxiety: our logical brain might object, but the anxiety persists. Most of us know that if we can bring ourselves to share these worries with other people, we will feel relieved.

Today, in the midst of the coronavirus pandemic, we all have both public and private worries. And while we might dismiss certain rumours publicly, we can carry the unease within us until we seek reassurance from a family member or friend later on. There are many, many ways to worry.

Perhaps the most astonishing feature of this situation is that, despite our familiarity with our own anxieties, we often fail to recognise that everyone else is just like us: full of secret worries. All the anxieties that I feel, other people feel them too. So, instead of thinking that you are burdening someone else with your worries, you should know that, deep down, other people share your concerns and have an equal need to connect. They need you just as much as you need them. Other people are just the same as us.

The greatest challenges to reaching out and sharing our worries are these psychological hesitations rather than any physical barriers. Of course, in the context of coronavirus, there may be physical barriers too. People who are ill or self-isolating are often most in need of sharing and support. But making the extra effort to connect, possibly by telephone or video-calling, can shift everyone's energies in a more positive and useful direction, and away from endless worries.

Thinking about other people and the world more broadly also diminishes our own individual anxiety.

It reminds us that this is not all about 'me'. In a sense, there is no 'me' with a problem like coronavirus; there is only 'us'. All health is public health. We can only manage this together.

The WHO Director-General emphasises the importance of this sense of 'solidarity' as a key element of the global response to coronavirus:

> This is a serious disease. It is not deadly to most people, but it can kill. We're all responsible for reducing our own risk of infection, and if we're infected, for reducing our risk of infecting others. There's something all of us can do to protect vulnerable people in our communities. That's why we keep talking about solidarity. This is not just a threat for individual people, or individual countries. We're all in this together, and we can only save lives together.

Conclusion

Viruses, epidemics, pandemics and panics are recurring features of human history. The global influenza pandemic of 1918 to 1920, also known as the Spanish flu, is, perhaps, the best-remembered pandemic of relatively recent times. Public health responses to these kinds of events have developed greatly over time, but psychological responses appear more constant: mixtures of complacency, appropriate anxiety, excessive anxiety and panic. All these responses are psychologically understandable, even though many of them do not help address the challenge at hand, and some even amplify the problems.

Against this background, responding to a pandemic such as the current outbreak of coronavirus involves a careful combination of public health measures, political determination and psychological awareness. While medical interventions are vital, they rarely achieve their goals without firm political support and an awareness that unhelpful psychological reactions can lead to hysteria, disengagement and nihilism. There can also be unjustified stigma and shame, social division and a tendency to assign blame to people perceived as spreading the virus or failing to contain it. None of this is helpful.

This book set out to provide some guidance about helpful psychological responses to coronavirus. While events such as personal illness, bereavements and other losses can present different kinds of challenges and can overwhelm us for periods, careful attention to the suggestions provided here will hopefully support us in building resilience when we can, help us to cope in the present circumstances, and leave us stronger if we face continued problems in the coming months. Here is a summary.

KNOWING

- *Do* **stay informed about coronavirus, but do not obsess.** Limit your media consumption about the virus to 15 minutes twice per day, focusing on reliable sources such as the WHO, national governments or a reliable newspaper. Ignore everything else about coronavirus for the rest of the day, unless it concerns you personally.

- *Don't* **fill in knowledge gaps with speculation or random musings on social media.** False or misleading information not only spreads myths but also reinforces our own anxieties and negative thought patterns. There are some things we simply do not know about coronavirus – yet.

- *Do* **try to know yourself better.** Take the time to consciously identify stresses and manage them as best as possible, and identify things that make you happy and optimise them as much as is feasible, albeit within the confines of social distancing or even self-isolation. Devoting conscious, deliberate attention to these tasks will help you navigate current and future challenges more mindfully and with greater self-awareness.

THINKING

- *Do* **focus on what you can control in this situation.** This is especially important when explaining coronavirus to children. It is useful to think of the well-known environmental slogan, 'Think global, act local'. Small actions (like hand-washing) matter greatly, both in the bigger picture and in our own lives.

- *Don't* **fall into unhelpful thinking habits.** It is useful to audit your thoughts from time to time, especially if you find yourself catastrophising, having continual negative automatic thoughts that affect your mood, selectively focusing on bad news or filtering inputs in a nihilistic way. Exercises such as thought-labelling can help greatly.
- *Do* **think of others.** We gain perspective when we see ourselves as part of a larger whole. Coronavirus has demonstrated just how inter-connected we all are. We can use this connectedness to strengthen each other and consolidate our response to this outbreak. The suffering of other people is continuous with our suffering – just as their happiness is continuous with ours.

FEELING

- *Do* **become more aware of your emotions.** While quarantine, self-isolation, limited social interaction and social distancing are effective public health measures, they create unusual social and emotional situations with which most people are unfamiliar. Recognising and labelling our emotions helps us to observe their power and accept them for what they are: transient feelings that will pass.

- *Don't* forget that emotions can disguise themselves as behaviours or facts – and can therefore mislead us. We can have several conflicting emotions at the same time or in quick succession. It is helpful if we practise the skill of sitting with uncomfortable emotions rather than responding to them immediately. Meditation helps, if we practise with compassion and consideration for ourselves. This takes time.

- *Do* talk to others about your feelings. If you want to be heard, listen. At a time of high anxiety, it is especially important that we label our feelings as emotions (rather than facts) and that we engage in direct, truthful communication (or, in Buddhist terminology, 'right speech'). No matter how difficult it might seem, the truth is our strength.

DOING

- *Do not* do things that increase panic without delivering any benefit. Follow the public health guidance provided by the WHO and national health authorities. Their advice applies to you. Adhering to their guidance will minimise your risk of contracting coronavirus, help protect other people and assist with keeping your anxiety in check. Their advice is based on the best available knowledge. Trust them. Going beyond their advice (e.g. wearing unnecessary face masks) can have negative effects (such as shortages of face masks for the sick and healthcare workers in other parts of the world). We need to stick together.

- *Do* **other things.** While social distancing, self-isolation and general anxiety can place certain limits on our activities, there is still plenty that we can do, both inside and outside: eat well, pay attention to sleep, go outside when possible and do some exercise. Also, find an activity that absorbs you and clears all your worries from your mind for a period of time: running, meditating, yoga, knitting or anything that clears and refreshes your mind.

- *Do* **reward yourself for your achievements and consciously practise compassion for yourself and others.** The current situation is difficult for everyone in different ways. Balancing sadness with hope is a real challenge, but it is possible. Focus on daily activities, short-term plans and cultivating compassion for everyone, including yourself.

BEING

- *Do* **remember that** *proportionality* **is the key.** Anxiety and panic can seem infinite, but nothing is truly infinite. While we cannot and should not ignore our emotions, we need to respond proportionately to them and leave room for logic, pragmatism and action. The coronavirus pandemic demands no less.

- *Do not* **project other life problems onto your anxiety about coronavirus.** For people who are not ill with coronavirus and do not have a family member affected, it is important to remember that while coronavirus is a serious problem that we need to manage, anxiety about the virus does not completely define us as people. This does not mean avoiding the urgent issues at hand. It means staying informed, keeping things in perspective and taking care of ourselves. We are always bigger than our anxiety.

- *Do* **find time to rediscover the value of being with other people.** We all have public and private worries. If we can connect with others – using whatever technology is necessary – we remind ourselves that we are not alone. Considering the needs of others also reinforces the point that we can only manage this situation together.

Final Thought

This is my proposed psychological toolkit for dealing with the anxiety and panic provoked by coronavirus. Managing anxiety is especially difficult in the present context because we cannot deny that there is something to be anxious about. But disproportionate anxiety and panic simply amplify the effects of the virus and hamper our response to it. Nobody benefits. Everyone suffers more.

I would like to place particular emphasis on the first section of this advice, 'Knowing'. Misinformation is an enormous threat, especially on social media. There is plenty of accurate information and reliable advice available for both the public and health professionals. We should heed it with care. The 'Further information' section at the end of this book presents reliable sources. We should be careful not to spread falsehoods inadvertently.

Once we are properly informed, the next step is to try to change what we do with the information that we have. Several sections of this book deal with this task. Broadly, it is useful to consciously think about our thinking habits and our feelings. To help with these tasks, we can practise contemplative techniques or other methods of becoming absorbed in the present moment and reflect on the world as big and us as small within it. This broadens our perspective as we develop compassion for ourselves and others, and, as Buddhism advises, move towards 'seeing reality as it really is', not how our anxious brains imagine it to be.

The urgency of the current pandemic underlines these needs to focus on reality, focus on compassion and focus on each other. Above all, we must simply keep going. At a time like this, we cannot let the problems of today blind us to the possibilities of tomorrow.

Small actions hold the key. In that spirit, if you have been reading this book on a computer, tablet or smartphone, please wipe down your device and wash your hands with care. Simple actions save lives.

Acknowledgements

I am very grateful to everyone who spoke with me and assisted with the preparation of this book. I particularly appreciate the support and guidance of my agent, Ms Vanessa O'Loughlin of the Inkwell Group (www.inkwellwriters.ie), and the team at Merrion Press, who are unfailingly superb (www.merrionpress.ie). Also, a special word of thanks to Latte Goldstein and the team at River Design (www.riverdesignbooks.com), who provided the superb cover for this book free of charge.

As ever, I remain deeply grateful to Regina, Eoin and Isabel, without whom none of this would be possible. I also greatly appreciate the support of my parents (Mary and Desmond), sisters (Sinéad and Niamh) and nieces (Aoife and Aisling), as well as the ongoing advice and guidance of Dr Larkin Feeney and Dr John Bruzzi. I am very grateful to Professor Veronica O'Keane, Ms Alison Collie and all of my other amazing colleagues at Trinity College Dublin and Tallaght University Hospital.

ACKNOWLEDGEMENTS

I still benefit from the wisdom and advice of my teachers at Scoil Chaitríona, Renmore, Galway; St Joseph's Patrician College, Nun's Island, Galway; and the School of Medicine at NUI Galway.

And, finally, a big thank you to my patients and their families, who have taught me everything that I know about illness, suffering, dignity, strength and recovery.

Further information

- The website of the World Health Organization (WHO) provides accurate, up-to-date information about corona-virus: www.who.int
- In the United Kingdom, the website of the National Health Service (NHS) has extensive information and advice: www.nhs.uk/conditions/coronavirus-covid-19
- In the United States, the Centers for Disease Control and Prevention (CDC) provides comprehensive resources: https://www.cdc.gov/coronavirus/2019-ncov/index.html
- In Ireland, consult the website of the Health Service Executive (HSE): www2.hse.ie/conditions/coronavirus/coronavirus.html They offer specific information about minding your mental health during the coronavirus outbreak: www2.hse.ie/wellbeing/mental-health/minding-your-mental-health-during-the-coronavirus-outbreak.html
- *The Lancet* medical journal has created a COVID-19 Resource Centre in order to assist health workers and researchers to bring this outbreak to an end. *The Lancet* COVID-19 Resource Centre brings together relevant content from across *The Lancet* journals as it is published

and all content listed on the page is free to access: www. thelancet.com/coronavirus

- The *BMJ* also has extensive coverage of the coronavirus outbreak, and many articles and resources are freely available on their website: www.bmj.com/coronavirus
- The Royal College of Psychiatrists in London offers online resources to help to deal with anxiety: www.rcpsych. ac.uk/mental-health/problems-disorders/anxiety-panic-and-phobias
- Several books and workbooks can also help with general anxiety:
    - Bourne, E.J., *The Anxiety and Phobia Workbook (Sixth Edition)* (Oakland, CA: New Harbinger Publications, Inc., 2015).
    - Boyes, A., *The Anxiety Toolkit: Strategies for Managing Your Anxiety So You Can Get on With Your Life* (London: Piatkus, 2015).
    - Chödrön, P., *When Things Fall Apart: Heart Advice for Difficult Times* (Boulder, CO: Shambala Publications, Inc., 2016).
    - Kabat-Zinn, J., *Full Catastrophe Living: How to Cope with Stress, Pain and Illness Using Mindfulness Meditation (Revised Edition)* (London: Piatkus, 2013).

Sources

INTRODUCTION

- Duan, L., Zhu, G., 'Psychological interventions for people affected by the COVID-19 epidemic', *Lancet Psychiatry*, 2020; pii: S2215-0366(20)30073-0. DOI: https://doi.org/10.1016/S2215-0366(20)30073-0 (accessed 15 March 2020).
- Health Service Executive (HSE) website (Ireland): www2.hse.ie/conditions/coronavirus/coronavirus.html (accessed 15 March 2020).
- Kelly, B.D., 'Coronavirus: should we keep calm and carry on?', *Guardian*, 9 March 2020. Courtesy of *Guardian* News & Media Ltd.
- *Lancet*, 'COVID-19: too little, too late?', *Lancet*, 2020; 395: 755. DOI: https://doi.org/10.1016/S0140-6736(20)30522-5 (accessed 15 March 2020).
- Ord, T., 'The importance of worst-case thinking', *Guardian*, 6 March 2020.
- Vetter, P., Eckerle, I., Kaiser, L., 'Covid-19: a puzzle with many missing pieces', *BMJ*, 2020; 368: m627. DOI: https://doi.org/10.1136/bmj.m627 (accessed 15 March 2020).

- World Health Organization (WHO), *Report of the WHO-China Joint Mission on Coronavirus Disease 2019 (COVID-19)* (Geneva: World Health Organization) (www.who.int/docs/default-source/coronaviruse/who-china-joint-mission-on-covid-19-final-report.pdf) (accessed 15 March 2020).
- World Health Organization (WHO) website: www.who.int (accessed 15 March 2020).
- Xu, X.W., Wu, X.X., Jiang, X.G., Xu, K.J., Ying, L.J., Ma, C.L., Li, S.B., Wang, H.Y., Zhang, S., Gao, H.N., Sheng, J.F., Cai, H.L., Qiu, Y.Q., Li, L.J., 'Clinical findings in a group of patients infected with the 2019 novel coronavirus (SARS-Cov-2) outside of Wuhan, China: retrospective case series', *BMJ*, 2020; 368: m606. DOI: https://doi.org/10.1136/bmj.m606 (Erratum in: *BMJ*, 2020; 368: m792) (accessed 15 March 2020).
- Yang, X., Yu, Y., Xu, J., Shu, H., Xia, J., Liu, H., Wu, Y., Zhang, L., Yu, Z., Fang, M., Yu, T., Wang, Y., Pan, S., Zou, X., Yuan, S., Shang, Y., 'Clinical course and outcomes of critically ill patients with SARS-CoV-2 pneumonia in Wuhan, China: a single-centered, retrospective, observational study', *Lancet Respiratory Medicine*, 2020; pii: S2213-2600(20)30079-5. DOI: https://doi.org/10.1016/S2213-2600(20)30079-5 (Erratum in: *Lancet Respiratory Medicine*, 2020; pii: S2213-2600(20)30103-X) (accessed 15 March 2020).

1. KNOWING

- Harford, T., 'Falsehoods spread and mutate just like a virus', *Financial Times*, 7–8 March 2020.

SOURCES

- Lanier, J., *Ten Arguments for Deleting Your Social Media Accounts Right Now* (New York: Henry Holt and Company, 2018).
- Ord, T., 'The importance of worst-case thinking', *Guardian*, 6 March 2020.
- Wang, V., 'Most cases of the illness are mild, a study finds', *New York Times (International Edition)*, 29 February–1 March 2020.
- Zarocostas, J., 'How to fight an infodemic', *Lancet*, 2020; 395: 676. DOI: https://doi.org/10.1016/S0140-6736(20)30461-X (accessed 15 March 2020).

2. THINKING

- Centers for Disease Control and Prevention, *Manage Anxiety & Stress* (Atlanta, GA: Centers for Disease Control and Prevention, 2020) (www.cdc.gov/coronavirus/2019-ncov/about/coping.html) (accessed 15 March 2020).
- Cookson, C., 'Beware fake news, do not panic buy and prepare for possible self-isolation', *Financial Times*, 7–8 March 2020.
- Kelly, B.D., *The Doctor Who Sat For A Year* (Dublin: Gill, 2019).
- Kelly, B.D., 'Panic and hysteria will only weaken effort to halt virus', *Irish Times*, 2 March 2020.

3. FEELING

- Brooks, S.K., Webster, R.K., Smith, L.E., Woodland, L., Wessely, S., Greenberg, N., Rubin, G.J., 'The psychological impact of quarantine and how to reduce it: rapid review of the evidence', *Lancet*, 2020; pii: S0140-6736(20)30460-8. DOI: https://doi.org/10.1016/S0140-6736(20)30460-8 (accessed 15 March 2020).

- Hellewell, J., Abbott, S., Gimma, A., Bosse, N.I., Jarvis, C.I., Russell, T.W., Munday, J.D., Kucharski, A.J., Edmunds, W.J., Centre for the Mathematical Modelling of Infectious Diseases COVID-19 Working Group, Funk, S., Eggo, R.M., 'Feasibility of controlling COVID-19 outbreaks by isolation of cases and contacts', *Lancet Global Health*, 2020; pii: S2214-109X(20)30074-7. DOI: https://doi.org/10.1016/S2214-109X(20)30074-7 (accessed 15 March 2020).

- Wang, G., Zhang, Y., Zhao, J., Zhang, J., Jiang, F., 'Mitigate the effects of home confinement on children during the COVID-19 outbreak', *Lancet*, 2020; pii: S0140-6736(20)30547-X. DOI: https://doi.org/10.1016/S0140-6736(20)30547-X (accessed 15 March 2020).

- Xiao, Y., Torok, M.E., 'Taking the right measures to control COVID-19', *Lancet Infectious Diseases*, 2020; pii: S1473-3099(20)30152-3. DOI: https://doi.org/10.1016/S1473-3099(20)30152-3 (accessed 15 March 2020).

4. DOING

- *Economist*, 'New world curriculum', *Economist*, 7 March 2020.

- Kelly, B.D., 'Are you dreaming of a good night's sleep?', *Irish Independent*, 5 February 2018.

- Kelly, B.D., *The Doctor Who Sat For A Year* (Dublin: Gill, 2019).

SOURCES

- Kelly, B.D., 'Panic and hysteria will only weaken effort to halt virus', *Irish Times*, 2 March 2020.
- Walker, M., *Why We Sleep: Unlocking the Power of Sleep and Dreams* (New York: Scribner/Simon & Schuster, Inc. 2017).
- World Health Organization (WHO), *Mental Health Considerations during COVID-19 Outbreak* (Geneva: World Health Organization, 2020) (www.who.int/docs/default-source/coronavirus/mental-health-considerations.pdf?sfvrsn=6d3578af_2) (accessed 15 March 2020).

5. BEING

- Devlin, H., Boseley, S., 'The essential guide: What do we know? How should we react?', *Guardian*, 7 March 2020.
- Jenkins, S., 'Let them wash your hands, but not your brain', *Guardian*, 7 March 2020.
- Mance, H., 'A shock to the system', *Financial Times*, 7–8 March 2020.
- Naughton, J., 'How a global health crisis turns into a state-run surveillance opportunity', *Observer*, 8 March 2020.
- Substance Abuse and Mental Health Services Administration, *Coping With Stress During Infectious Disease Outbreaks* (Rockville, MD: Substance Abuse and Mental Health Services Administration, 2014) (https://store.samhsa.gov/system/files/sma14-4885.pdf) (accessed 15 March 2020).

- World Health Organization (WHO), *Mental Health Considerations during COVID-19 Outbreak* (Geneva: World Health Organization, 2020) (www.who.int/docs/default-source/coronaviruse/mental-health-considerations.pdf?sfvrsn=6d3578af_2) (accessed 15 March 2020).
- WHO Director-General, *WHO Director-General's opening remarks at the media briefing on COVID-19 (5 March 2020)* (Geneva: World Health Organization, 2020) (www.who.int/dg/speeches/detail/who-director-general-s-opening-remarks-at-the-media-briefing-on-covid-19---5-march-2020) (accessed 15 March 2020).

CONCLUSIONS

- Camus, A., *The Plague* (London: Hamish Hamilton, 1948).
- Chödrön, P., *When Things Fall Apart: Heart Advice for Difficult Times* (Boulder, CO: Shambala Publications, Inc., 1997) (2016).
- Foley, C., *The Last Irish Plague: The Great Flu Epidemic in Ireland, 1918–19* (Dublin and Portland, OR: Irish Academic Press, 2011).
- Garcia, M.N., Hernandez, D., Gorchakov, R., Murray, K.O., Hotez, P.J., 'The 1899 United States kissing bug epidemic', *PLoS Neglected Tropical Diseases*, 2015; 9: e0004117. DOI: https://doi.org/10.1371/journal.pntd.0004117 (accessed 15 March 2020).
- Giuffrida, A., '"This is so surreal". Stigma and strain in Italy as EU's worst outbreak intensifies', *Guardian*, 7 March 2020.

SOURCES

- Honigsbaum, M., *The Pandemic Century: One Hundred Years of Panic, Hysteria and Hubris* (London: C. Hurst and Co. [Publishers] Ltd., 2019).
- Honigsbaum, M., 'Spanish influenza redux: revisiting the mother of all pandemics', *Lancet*, 2018; 391: 2492-5. DOI: https://doi.org/10.1016/S0140-6736(18)31360-6 (accessed 15 March 2020).
- Kelly, B.D., 'Panic and hysteria will only weaken effort to halt virus', *Irish Times*, 2 March 2020.
- *Lancet*, 'COVID-19: fighting panic with information', *Lancet*, 2020; 395: 537. DOI: https://doi.org/10.1016/S0140-6736(20)30379-2 (accessed 15 March 2020).
- Razai, M.S., Doerholt, K., Ladhani, S., Oakeshott, P., 'Coronavirus disease 2019 (covid-19): a guide for UK GPs', *BMJ*, 2020; 368: m800. DOI: https://doi.org/10.1136/bmj.m800 (Erratum in: *BMJ*, 2020; 368: m989) (accessed 15 March 2020).
- Robins, J., *The Miasma: Epidemic and Panic in Nineteenth Century Ireland* (Dublin: Institute of Public Administration, 1995).